SUPER NARWHAL
AND JELLY JOLT

BEN CLANTON

SCHOLASTIC INC.

FOR THEO!
MY SUPER SON!

ISBN 978-1-338-28272-6

Text and illustrations copyright © 2017 by Ben Clanton. All rights reserved. Published by Scholastic Inc., 557 Broadway, New York, NY 10012, by arrangement with Tundra Books, a division of Penguin Random House Canada Limited. SCHOLASTIC and associated logos are trademarks and/or registered trademarks of Scholastic Inc.

18   21 22 23

Printed in the U.S.A.   40

First Scholastic printing, April 2018

Edited by Tara Walker and Jessica Burgess
Designed by Ben Clanton and Andrew Roberts
The super-duper artwork in this book was rendered in colored pencil, watercolor, ink and colored digitally.
The text was handlettered by Ben Clanton.

Photos: (waffle) © Tiger Images/Shutterstock; (strawberry) © Valentina Razumova/Shutterstock; (pickle) © dominitsky/Shutterstock; (tuba) Internet Archive Book Images

CONTENTS

swoosh!

I'M GOING TO BECOME A SUPERHERO!

HOW ABOUT...

SUPER NARWHAL !!!

HMMM...CATCHY. BUT WHAT ABOUT A SECRET IDENTITY?

LET'S SEE... WHAT ELSE?

YOU'RE GOING TO NEED A SIDEKICK!

YEP! A REALLY SUPER FRIEND...

WHO? SHARK? OCTOPUS? TURTLE?

YOU, OF COURSE!

REALLY?! SUPER! BUT WHAT SHOULD MY NAME BE? STING? BLUE LIGHTNING? NO...I'VE GOT IT!

JELLY JOLT
THE SUPER SIDEKICK!

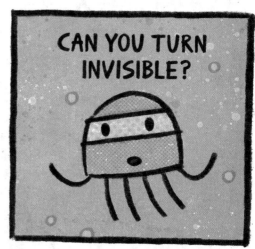

CAN YOU FLY? BREATHE FIRE?
ANYTHING?

NARWHAL, YOU CAN'T BE A SUPERHERO WITHOUT A SUPERPOWER!

I'M SURE I'LL COME UP WITH SOMETHING! BUT FIRST...

...THERE IS SOMETHING SUPER IMPORTANT TO DO.

SAVE THE WORLD?

swoosh!

SUPER SEA CREATURES

REAL SEA CREATURES WITH REAL SUPER-AWESOME ABILITIES

THE MIMIC OCTOPUS CAN CHANGE ITS COLOR, SHAPE AND MOVEMENTS TO LOOK LIKE OTHER SEA LIFE SUCH AS SNAKES, LIONFISH, STINGRAYS AND JELLYFISH.

STOP COPYING ME!

STOP COPYING ME!

DOLPHINS SLEEP WITH ONLY HALF OF THEIR BRAIN AND WITH ONE EYE OPEN TO WATCH FOR THREATS.

DOLPHINS CAN ALSO "SEE" INSIDE MANY ANIMALS BY USING SOUND WAVES.

I SEE YOU HAD A WAFFLE FOR LUNCH!

BLUE WHALES ARE ONE OF THE LOUDEST ANIMALS ON EARTH.

HI!!!...

NO NEED TO SHOUT!

CRABS CAN REGROW CLAWS OR LEGS IF THEY LOSE ONE IN A FIGHT.

YOU'RE MISSING A CLAW!

MEH... IT'LL GROW BACK.

FLYING FISH CAN GLIDE UP TO 400 m (1,300 ft.) AND TRAVEL AT SPEEDS OF MORE THAN 70 km/h (43 mph). EVEN FASTER, THOUGH, IS THE SAILFISH, WHICH CAN REACH SPEEDS OF UP TO 110 km/h (68 mph).

EAT MY BUBBLES!

ZOOM

NARWHAL, YOU'RE

A SUPERSTAR!

SOUNDS STELLAR!

...I'D LIKE TO BE UP THERE! IN THE SKY! A REAL STAR!

MAYBE I AM A REAL STAR, BUT I FELL TO EARTH AND HIT MY HEAD OR SOMETHING AND NOW I DON'T REMEMBER!

MAYBE! WANT ME TO TRY THROWING YOU UP THERE?

OKAY!

SPLASH!

SUPER WAFFLE
AND STRAWBERRY SIDEKICK!

by Narwhal and Jelly

OH NO! A GIANT BUTTER BLOB IS ATTACKING THE CITY!

EEK!

MOMMY!

YIP! YIP! YIP!

RAWR!

SUPER WAFFLE AND STRAWBERRY SIDEKICK TO THE RESCUE!

SUPER NARWHAL!

OR DID THAT MUSTACHE
YOU'VE NEVER HAD SET
YOUR HAIR ON FIRE,
STICK YOU IN A TUBA
WITH A PIRATE PIG
AND CALL YOU A
BLUE-FOOTED
BOOBY?

OH, WAIT, NOW I REMEMBER...

WHOA! I CAN'T BELIEVE IT! YOUR SUPERPOWER IS THE POWER TO BRING OUT THE SUPER IN OTHERS!

SUPERFY!